THE NAUGHTY DIARY
OF AN
EDWARDIAN
LADY

The publishers would like to thank Penelope Bishop-Prigg Smythe, Ethel Hordle's great niece, who discovered the original diary in her great-aunt's old chest, on turning out the contents of her modest, fifty-room country cottage. Thanks are also due to Michael and Jackie Ridley and Bryan Neary, whose untiring work at editing and spoof-reading have made this book possible. The proceeds will be used to prevent Penelope's family pile from collapsing.

Copyright © Origination 1981

First published in 1981 in Great Britain by Macdonald · London and Sydney

Macdonald Futura Publishers Ltd., Paulton House, 8 Shepherdess Walk, London N1 7LW, in association with Origination, 8 The Square, Puddletown, Dorset DT2 8SL

ISBN 0 354 04690 X

Printed and bound in Hong Kong by Toppan Printing Co.

THE NAUGHTY DIARY OF AN EDWARDIAN LADY

A facsimile reproduction of a naturist's diary
for the year 1906. Ethel Hordle recorded
in words and paintings her affairs
and flirtations in the British
countryside and playgrounds
of Europe through the
changing seasons
of the year.

MACDONALD
MACDONALD FUTURA PUBLISHERS
LONDON

Rake's Bottom
Maiden-under-Mann
Middlesex

Ethel Hordle.

MATURE NOTES

FOR

1906

" To sit on rocks, to love o'er flood and fell;
To lowly grace the forest's shady scene,
Where things of manly passion dwell.
And mortal foot hath ne'er or barely been!
To climb the trackless mountain to unseen eye,
With the wild young smock, who never needs a goad;
Together o'er leaps and falls to lean and lie;
'Tis not solicitude, 'tis but to hold his
Natural charms; and view his stores unrolled."

By Ron.

JANUARY

Named after the Roman god Janus, who's always shown with two faces, looking in opposite directions ~ anterior and posterior.

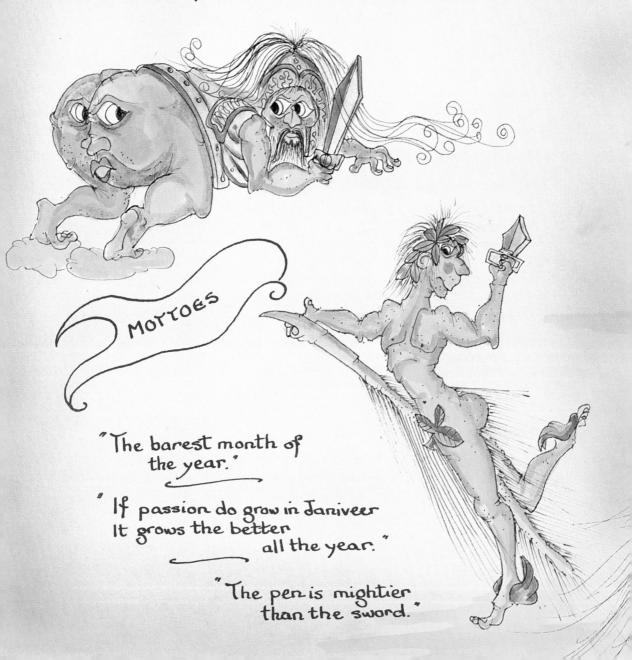

MOTTOES

"The barest month of the year."

"If passion do grow in Janiveer It grows the better all the year."

"The pen is mightier than the sword."

A bright New Year's
morning

January

Jan 1. New Year's Day. A bright New Year's morning, so I'm told. Did not awoke until 4 in the afternoon. Not sure what happened last night, where I am, or who it is thats beside me in bed. Can't find my knickers.

5. Staying at Inebreate Hall, Chippingsodbury, guest of Lord Clutterbuck, 5th Viscount of something or other.

11. Very cold so played indoor games. Geoffrey Pinchbottom's rather nice but does nothing - but stare.

12. Woke early, heard some birds singing in the garden. Looking through the window, I could see nothing but Arum, the gardener. He looked up and saw two blue tits at the window.

18. Geoffrey Pinchbottom finally thawed and chased me across the lake. At last the ice is broken.

Blue Tits

JANUARY

Jan. 23. Visited the small wood at the back of the house to pick some catkins. On moving some of the thick leaves on the evergreen bushes between the trees, I discovered Violet, my maid, covered by wild Arum, the gardener. While they rolled, clinging lightly to each other, I noticed her white skin flushed with passion ~ reminding me of the pink roses of Spring. Their wild cries merged with the busy sounds of the wood. Unnoticed, I gently moved away, wondering whether this early sowing of wild oats would bring a new maid.

24. Exhausted by Geoffrey and Inebreate Hall, I took the 9.45 train back to the peace of Rake's Bottom.

Wild Arum
and
Violet

FEBRUARY

This is the month of love and of Saint Valentine. It is my favourite month and February 14th. my favourite day.

Birthdays. Feb 9. Richard Fitzbuckall ♡
Feb 16. Rodney Lusterton. ♡♡♡
Feb 27 'Tiny' Quellbynight ♡♡♡♡♡♡

"All the months of the year
Do envy fair Februeer"

"In February, if thou hearest thunder
'Tis nearly sounds of hearts a pounder."

"If February brings no change of love:
Fair Eros Try again."

"Unarm Eros; the long days task is done
And we must sleep."

February

"One month is past, another is begun,
Since merry bells rang out the dying year,
And blooms of rarest beauty gladly peer,
As if impatient for some vernal fun;
And through the darkest night 'till darkness all is dun;
The virgin snowdrop, filled with touching fire,
Plays 'till cold morning, and only then to tire,
And with the light, the winsome little one
Becomes a primrose."

Hardly Coleridge.

Fair Maids
of
February

February

Feb 1. Dull day pouring with rain. All the signs are that it will be a wild, lusty and stormy month.

2. I read in 'The Times' that Valentine's balls are being held by Felicity de Knockers, The Hon. Basil Lovelace, Sir John Prickleton, Licentious Wiggle, the artist, and others. It promises to be quite a passionate time.

9. Snow covers the ground like a white sheet, but the sun broke through early to change the white to a golden hue. The Aspen sisters of Groat Willow, apparently affected by the scene danced wildly in the sunshine. The birds too enjoyed it. At one time there were eight Tits bouncing about, including a pair of Great Tits. Julia Aspen is a buxom sixteen.

12. Left for The Hon Basil Lovelace's seat at Piddle Upton in Dorset. I've known Daisy Lovelace, his daughter, since Rodine, we hope to have a simply delightful time. Everyone who is anyone is coming to the ball at Ashburn House. William took me to the railway station in the trap - such a nice strong boy. The journey to Piddle Upton was tiresome. There was this horrid man - a pipe major in the Fraser Highlanders who kept dropping his batton at my feet, then groping and making overtures to my legs to recover it. His sporran kept jumping up and down each time. Upon my garter travelling by train takes all the incentive out of life. In other circumstances - I might have been tempted.

13. Tomorrow the grand fancy dress ball.

'She who has never loved has never lived.' John Gay.

Love looks not with the eyes
but with the mind;
And therefore is winged
Cupid painted blind.

Shakespeare.

It was the merry month of February
When young men in their jolly roguery
Rose early in the morn 'fore break of day
To seek them valentines so trim and gay.
With whom they may consort in summer
sheen,
And dance the high degree on our town
green.

Thomas Naske

The powers of love so powerful are,
What mortal can withstand,
Or, who can say oppose they dare
Where Cupid bears command
This damsel quickly she did yield
The youngsters skill to try,
The twinkling Archer won the Field,
And then she down
did lie.

Anon.

February

Fancy dress
always brings out
my best points.

"Wee, modest, crimson-tipped flower
Thou's met me in an evil hour;
For I maun crush among the stoure
        Thy slender stem.
To spare thee now is past my power
        Thou bonnie gem.

There in thy scanty mantle clad
Thy snowy bosom sunward spread
Thou lifts thy unassuming head
        In humble guise
But now the share uptears thy bed
        And low thou lies."

Robert Burns.

"On sunny days there in the shade
Beneath the trees reclined a maid
Who lifted up her dress (she said)
To keep the moonbeams off her head."

Daisy
(Bellis Lovelace)

February

Feb 14. Saint Valentine's Day. Although there was a sharp frost, the sun shone all day. I received twelve Valentines~ some of them quite naughty. A few were delivered in person and others sent with divine tokens of love. Godfrey de Bellamount sent a charming diamond and emerald brooch, while Lusty Foggerty sent me something to remember him by, in silver, with a ruby tip. Several equally lovely trinkets were sent anon. My darling husband Horatio is still somewhere up the Amazon. I do hope he is enjoying things as much as I. Maybe he will find a little native girl. They say primitives are skillfull lovers. There is much to explore~ I am making discoveries all the time. It's nearly a year now since I've seen H.H.~ but what can one expect when one marries an explorer with lots of lovely money. It's wonderful how friends rally round~ I never feel cold in bed.
Daisy's ball was a great success, everyone had a simply wonderful time. It was a stroke of genius to hold it in fancy dress. One felt far freer, in fact I'm not at all sure what happened. I think I ended up with the rooster. Even without his costume he was a wily old cock~ that much I do remember.

Feb 23. February is nearly out. It came in lying down and if things go on as they are I shall be flat on my back when it goes out. Top marks to Martin Goldfinch last night.

By Gis and by Saint Charity
Alack and fie for shame!
Young men will do't, if they come to't;
By cock they are to blame.

Shakespeare

March

Gusty Foggerty
letting off steam.

MARCH

Mar. 4. Lusty Foggerty, that gas-bag, took me up in his balloon. I'm afraid the thin air proved too much for him for he lost control and tried to ravish me. I warned him to control himself and not to prick the balloon. It all ended with our having to disgard ballast, infact anything, to keep it up. It's terribly difficult to take off a corset in a basket.

Mar. 10. Tried out a new game with Jeremy Withertool — strip rummy. Down to nothing, we drew. Laying my cards on the table I saw he had nothing to hide. He said he had to hand it to me — for he was really a novice. He must think I was born yesterday, but I enjoyed it.

March Mottoes.

'A peck of March lust
 is worth a king's randy son'.

'The worm in March
 Goes in like a lion
 Comes out like a lamb'.

"March winds the raiments strip
 Exposed lies the mount of
   pleasure
 And in its valley, the hare."

March ramming

'No man who has
wrestled with a
self-adjusting
card table can
ever quite be
the man he
once was.'

J. Thurber.

" He blushed, that being youthful, hot and lusty.
He proved neither youth, nor man, but old and rusty.
Nay more, I did not distain a whit
To take it in my hand and play with it.
But then I saw it would by no means stand
But still drooped down, regarding not my hand."

after Ovid.

'The only way to get rid of temptation
is to yield to it.'

Oscar Wilde.

March.

Mar. 20. Glorious sunshine. Went for a walk across Tumble-rake Down, near Dead Wood, and saw Celandine Alderfoot and Procumbent Field Speedwell. Celandine is blossoming out now, showing all her little anthers and filaments. She was lying in the grass with Robin Hawthorn of Cobbler's Cottage. Spring was bursting all around, with downy balls and spears, like lance heads of willow and daffodil, exhibiting themselves unashamed of their nakedness. Went to London by carriage for Trotty Hicks' little soirée. I wish G.B. would stop assessing my assets. It's the same with all these bankers - so calculating.

Mar. 25. Violet is a little pale, but blooming.

The portion of a woman that appeals to man's depravity
Is constructed with extraordinary care,
And what at first appears to be a simple little cavity
  Is really an elaborate affair.

Now doctors of distinction have examined these phenomena
On numbers of experimental dames,
And classified the organs of the feminine abdomina
And given them delightful Latin names.

So isn't it a pity when we common people chatter
Of the mysteries to which I have referred,
We should use for such a delicate and complicated matter
Such a short and unattractive little word.

Anon

March

The winds of March
blew right up the
brass steps of the
carriage.

APRIL

April (French Avril) is female. The name of the month being derived from the Greek word for "opening". Some say that it is dedicated to women because the first day of the month is All Fools' Day ~ by my experience it should be masculine. April Fools' Day is always good for a lark. It is also Spring ~ and in Spring a young man's fancy turns to love ~ and in love men are such fools — but, oh, such adorable fools.

Days of note:

    April 1. All Fools' Day
    April 20. Anniversary of my loosing my virginity

    April 29 Horatio's birthday

Mottoes.

    'The silliest woman can manage a clever man; but it needs a very clever woman to manage a fool.'
                    Rudyard Kipling

    ' 'Tis an old maxim in the schools,
    That flattery's the food of fools;
    Yet now and then your men of wit
    Will condescend to take a bit.'
                    Jonathan Swift

APRIL

"When Daisy's red and Violet's blue   And cuckold's bed of yellow hue
This lady mocks the silver knight   Becomes a meadow of delight."

APRIL

7. Very cloudy day, big cumulus set against a brigt blue sky. I walked by the water mill at Trickletorrent Brook and bumped into Jack, the miller. He was pleased to see me and said he had something really beautiful to show me and put his hand in his trousers to find it. After a few minutes of fumbling around he seemed to get most frustrated and embarrassed. I told him not to get excited and make a big thing of it ~ he could always show it to me when he felt like it some other time.

12. A letter came today from Horatio ~ he is now on board The Inquisitor, sailing southwards towards Patagonia.

16. A glorious day of bright sunshine. Marigold and I went for a walk across the downs. Everywhere was bathed in the gold of wild daffodils

20. Another lovely day with bright sunshine. Went to Bath with James Allspice. It took all day to reach there but the journey was lightened by the good weather and company. We arrived at his house at The Crescent in good time for dinner ~ although somewhat in a state of undress.

I can tell you, and I will,
Of my lady's water mill.
She rode to mill upon a horse
Yet was she maiden not the worse
I laid she down upon a sack
To the miller called she Jack

Strike softly said she, hurt not my back
And spare not, let the mill clack
Jack was full nice
And would be willing at a trice
His millstones set between a screw
Charms not known but to a few.

This maid to mill did oft resort
And of her game made no report.

Traditional

A thing of beauty
is a joy for ever.
Keats.

"Licence my roving hands,
and let them go
Before, behind, above,
below."

John Donne 1573-1631

Riding Bristol fashion

APRIL

21. The seventh consecutive day of bright sunshine. Went riding with James Allspice. It was a mad, exciting day. Galloping across the fields we jumped a fence, and one of the horses stumbled, knocking us both off our saddles. James fell on top of me. I could see him as he erected himself. He looked at me, dazzled, then examined his mount to see if she was still able to give him a ride. I'm glad to say I was fine, being quite used to tumbles. We carried on riding Bristol fashion. Later in the day the heavens opened unexpectedly and we had to take refuge in a barn. Soaked through we stripped to dry off. It never rains but it pours. I know I should not let things get on top of me but I do, but then I really quite enjoy it. It was a divine day.

30. Found beautiful primrose in the bog.

"With Oh, and Oh, she itching moves her hips
And to and fro, full lightly starts and skips.
She jerks her legs, and sprawleth with
                              her heels,
No tongue may tell the solace that she
                              feels."

Thomas Nashe

APRIL

"England is the paradise of women,
the purgatory of men
and the hell of horses."

John Florio 1553-1625

This maid was careless, and withall,
  She rather took, then got a fall:
The wanton rambler chanced to see
  Part of her leg's sincerity:

And ravished thus, it came to pass,
  The nag, like to the Prophet's ass
Began to speak, and would have been
  A telling what rare sights he'd seen:
And had told all; but did refrain,
  Because his tongue was tied again.

after Herrick 1591-1674

MAY

The fifth month of the year, but the third of the ancient Roman calendar. May is supposed to be named after Maia, the mother of Mercury. In former days in Olde Englande, May-day was the name given to the first day of the month and the occasion for many festivities celebrating spring and fertility, which had their roots in pagan times, including dancing around the May-pole and crowning the May-queen. It was once general in the country for young maidens to dance and rejoice around the May-pole, a large erection, sometimes bedecked with ribbon. It is said that village youths used to vie with each other to de-flower the Mayflower.

Special Days.　May 1.　May Day.
　　　　　　　May 23.　J. B.'s day.

May Mottoes.

"He was as fresh as
is the month of May."
　　　　　　　Chaucer.

"At Christmas I no more desire a rose.
Than wish a snow in May's newfangled
　　　　　　　　　　　　shows."
　　　　　　　　　　　　Shakespeare.

Who doffs his clothes on a winter's day
Will gladly take them off for May (or June or Ethel!)

MAY

Fly fishing

Green grow the rushes O,
The sweetest hours that
e'er I spent,
Are spent among
the lasses O!

R. Burns.

MAY

Shall I compare thee to a summer's day?
Thou art more lovely and more temperate.
Rough winds do shake the darling buds of May,
And summer's lease hath all too short a date.

Sonnet 18. Shakespeare.

Then, as the empty bee, that lately bore,
Into the common treasure, all her store,
Flies 'bout the painted field with nimble wing
Deflowering the fresh virgins of the Spring;

Thomas Carew 1595~1640

And twixt her paps like early fruit in May,
    Whose harvest seemed to hasten now apace:
They loosely did their wanton wings display,
    And there to rest themselves did boldly place.
Sweet thoughts I envy yourso happy rest,
    Which oft I wished, yet never was so blessed.

Spencer.

A man in the bush
        is worth
    two in the open.

MAY

May 1. May Day. Went to the village square where a number of young maidens danced around the May-pole that young Dan Hawthorn had erected. A number of brightly coloured ribbons hung down from the tip. The forces of spring seemed to have affected everyone, for in Devil's Meadow a group of Morris men were chasing Lily and her friends through the bushes, singing loudly all the time. Alongside the stream that runs across the bottom of the meadow was a fine display of Marigold and Ladies' Smocks strewn on the bank. It was very close and sultry. I wish I could be a May-queen again ~ I do so like being chased, especially caught.

> "O gie the lass her fairin' lad,
>   O gie the lass her fairin',
> An' something else she'll gie to you,
>   That's waly worth the wearin';
> Syne coup her o'er amang the creels,
>   When ye hae taen your brandy,
> The mair she bangs the less she squeels,
>   An' hey for houghmagandie."
>   Robert Burns

MAY

May 6. Went for a walk across the fields and came upon Cherry and young Hawthorn. A wonderful sight just now, the masses of snowy pink bossom making a striking contrast with the deep gold of the gorse.

11. Another letter from my dear Horatio. A colleague of his, Donald Portcullis, the expedition's palaeontologist, has found the most wonderful remains of ancient man, which he has called Homo-erectus portcullis ~ I thought all men are Homo-erectus.

14. A very exhausting day-and-a-bit travelling up to Glen Barren to stay with MacNess of MacNess. It was lovely to see Nessie again.

16. Went fly-fishing with Nessie. The banks of the river were very popular with the birds. Saw Robin place his morsel in a little cavity of a tree where his family was waiting.

20. Fishing again. It's lovely to have virtually the whole estate to ourselves ~ no prying eyes. Our favourite spot is by the rush beds. Needless to say we hardly have time to catch fish!

25. Mac Perriwinkle, Nessie's piper, offered me his bagpipes to play with. It was quite a lark considering his tassels were hanging out.

"A man that is young in years may be old in hours, if he hath lost no time."
Francis Bacon 1561-1626

"Give me chastity and continence — but not yet." St Augustin 354-430

From 20 to 30 if a man lives right
It is once in the morning and twice at night;
From 30 to 40 if he still lives right
He misses a morning and sometimes a night;
From 40 to 50 it is now and then;
From 50 to 60 it is God knows when;
From 60 to 70 if he is still inclined:
But don't let him kid you, it is still
                              in his mind.

His sporting days are over,
His little light is out;
What used to be his sex appeal
Is now his water spout.
It used to be embarrassing
To make the thing behave
For nearly every morning
It stood and watched him shave.
But now it's getting older,
It sure gives him the blues
To have it dangling down his legs
And watch him clean his shoes.

Anon

JUNE

William Worborough
feeling young.

JUNE

June, a month for bursting forth ~ the month of ripening. The sixth month of the year but the fourth according to the old Roman calendar, it gets its name from Juno, the sister and wife of the god Jupiter. It was the Sear (dry) monath of the Saxons.

Special Days. June 21. Summer Solstice.
June 24. Midsummer Day

My Mottoes for June.

"Words may be false and full of art,
Sighs are the natural language
of the heart."
Thomas Shadwell 1642-1692

"Man has his will ~ but woman has her way."
Oliver Wendell Holmes 1809-1894

"Every man is wanted, and no man is wanted much."
Ralph Waldo Emerson 1803-1882

"Variety's the very spice of life
That gives it all its flavour."
William Cowper 1731-1800

"Every man loves what he's good at."
Thomas Shadwell

JUNE

"To travel hopefully
is a better thing
than to arrive."

Robert Louis Stevenson

The Order of the Garter

June 1   Stormy beginning to what I hope will be a bright, sunny month.

3.   Travelled back to Rake's Bottom ~ I really enjoyed my time with Nessie. Its wonderful that Horatio and he are such friends.

7.   William Warborough, Duke of Tinkleton, collected me in his new horseless carriage, a Yellow Hammer Speedwell Mark III, intending to drive to Newhaven where we were to take the P.S. Paris to Dieppe. Unfortunately we had a spot of bother on the way and I had to lend him my garter to make an emergency repair. As we were so delayed we had to seek lodgings at The Lovers' Nest Inn near Small Heath. William made the most of his broken water pump ~ and the night.

8.   Left William's vehicle with the Hon. Gerald Ambergriss at Kissin-Bush House, and boarded the "Paris" for Dieppe. From Dieppe we took the train to Paris where we were met by the Marquis d'arce.

14.   Paris is so romantic ~ I've had so many encounters, most of them nocturnal (though the time of day doesn't seem to matter so much here) that I haven't had time to write in my diary.

16.   Went to see M. Eifel's magnificent erection.

18.   Glorious evening at Moulin Rouge. My escort told me of a funny little French man, no taller than my thigh, who used to sketch the clients and artistes. Then I thought he said I was too loose with my affections ~ but I later found out he was only telling me the name of the artist.

JUNE

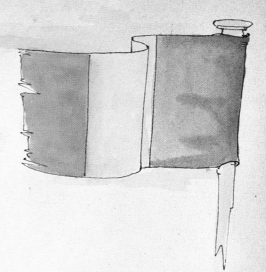

For you dream you are crossing
the Channel,
And tossing about in a steamer
from Harwich ~
Which is something between a large
bathing machine
And a very small second~class
carriage

W. S. Gilbert

"Travel, in the younger sort, is a part
of education; in the elder, a part
of experience."

Francis Bacon 1561-1626

"I never travel without my
diary. One should always
have something sensational
to read on the train."

Oscar Wilde

JUNE

June 18. (cont.) These French would be so much more civilized if they followed our example and spoke English. The cabaret was exhilarating, especially the finale when we were raided by the constabulary. In the confusion I was separated from my escort and was arrested with the dancers. One rather cheeky gendarme had quite a time searching me~ my clothing was loose, but that was no excuse for him to examine my assets.

Locked up all night in a French jail, I made the most of the situation when the jailer, Pierre Napoleon, paid me more attention than he should. My French is not that good, and although French, he was not a man of letters, and dispite his position, I could not condom it. Actually he was quite nice and the bottles of wine he brought were excellent. By the early morning Napoleon lay exhausted on the floor~ he had met his Waterloo, 91 years to the day after his namesake, and Josephine (alias E.H.) had triumphed.

June 19. Released with apologies.
June 24. Midsummer's Day. Took the train with William to St Tropez. The South of France is lovely and warm at this time of year.

"Anyone who has been to an English public school will always feel comparatively at home in a prison."
before E. Waugh

cherchez la femme

trois fillettes

Entente cordiale

JULY

In 46 B.C. Julius Caesar, on doing some calculations one day, found that the Romans were 90 days in advance of real time in their year. He worked out by looking at the Sun, that a year should have about 365¼ days – he therefore reshuffled the months. July, the seventh month is named after him. Unfortunately he had a few minutes left over and this gradually mounted up until in 1582 Pope Gregory said stop, did a new sum, and altered the calendar yet again.

Special Days.

July 4.   American Independence Day. (1776)
July 8.   Cynthia's Independence Day (1905)
July 14. Storming of the Bastille (1789)
July 15. St Swithin
July 25. Reginald Lloyd's Birthday

July Mottoes.

"Summer has set in
    with its usual severity."
                    Coleridge

"My beautiful lady goes to see the flowers,
And a flower, she forgets, is she:
Would they not come to blossom in her bowers
Should flowers intellegent be?"

                    Yuen Mei 1716–1797

JULY

July 1. Staying at a charming hotel, the Coq d'or. It is really very quaint, especially the notices pinned up in the rooms. I must copy them down:

NOTICE

Each chamber faces the sea has a french widow included and will be charged for services. Each bed has been tested for satisfaction by a chamber maid who will attend your desires during the night. She can be called by dangling the bell. Swimming in the sea is without clothes but bath costumes are not giving to the morals offence. In case of flagellation please use sand bucket then hall garçon. Please do not make passes or scandels or make use of chains or percussion instruments after midnight or in establishments of public use. Leather or rubber garments may be worn and taken off for the house maid to attend to. Please show your feelings to the Madam.

MENU FOR CONSUMMATION

Cock soap
Consummate

Whores of Dover
Muscle mermaid

Peasant with Brazen Cock
Wild fuck with orange sorts

Pomme tittes
Cabitch French Pis Raped Carrots

Eyes Creme

The tarts of the house of your choice are available for your delight.

July 3. The sun and sands here are so relaxing.

JULY

July 4. Had a wonderful night with Dusky Cranebill, an American Senator, staying at the hotel. We celebrated American Independence Day. After several bottles of champagne, he insisted on showing me how he rides bronco fashion

8. The sun and sands here are so relaxing.

14. Fête Nationale. Great festivities in the town, marking the storming of the Bastille in 1789. It was marked in my bedroom by a terrible mix-up. It seems, somewhat inebriated, I made assignations with William, Dusky and a French man I had met called Jacques Custarde — all at the same time. They appeared, one after the other, until all three were there, ready, willing, but because of circumstances, not able. With some discrete juggling I'm glad to say things were eventually sorted out to everyone's satisfaction — not least to mine.

I do wish Horatio would return, life would be much less complicated.

20. Travelled back to Paris

"I come, I come; sweet lady by thy leave,
Softly my fingers, up this curtain heave
And make me happy stealing by degrees
First bare her legs, then creep up her knees."

Thomas Nashe

JULY

July 23. Went to François Gayhomme, who does women's things, to buy some new gowns. We had something of a tussle with my cami knickers which got caught in my feminine gender ~ but he seemed like a nice boy.

27. Went shopping in Paris ~ everything is so divinely à la mode. Had a terrible mishap to my bodice (which was feeling the strain) and popped out for a while. I was forced into an erection to mans' supremacy to make emergency repairs. A friendly French man offered me a helping hand ~ but I managed without it.

An erection to mans' supremacy.
Paris 1906.

AUGUST

August, the eighth month of the year is named after the extremely vain Roman emperor Augustus. The month was so named because it was not fatal to him, infact it was extremely lucky. He wanted to give it more days than any other month but days were in short supply, so he had to settle for thirty-one.

Special Days. Augustus decreed that all days in August were special. I tend to agree with him.

Poem for August.

" Kissing and glancing, soothing, all make way
But to the acting of this private play:
Name it I would; but being blushed red,
The rest I'll speak,
   when we meet both in bed."
                              Robert Herrick

AUGUST

tending my convolvulus

AUGUST

Aug. 1. Lovely warm day, an English summer's day at its best.

7. Spent the day packing in readiness for the journey to Scotland on the 9th.

10. Arrived at Abertartan. Staying on the MacQuim estate, on the banks of Loch Tidlewinkie. Everyone is gathering for the glorious 12th.

11. Walked over the moors with Andrew Mac-Quim. Came across Heather in the big bog. Everywhere was covered with a purple mantle.

12. The Glorious 12th. I partnered Ian MacQuim, Andrew's elder brother — he will be Laird. Wearing our sporting clothes, we strolled over Heather Moor. Sensing game, he flushed a cock from the bushes, raised his barrel in a meaningful manner and fired. He was flushed with success. He tried again, but he had shot his bolt and could not get another up the spout quick enough. He had a grouse at this but soon got over it. I find we are birds of a feather.

15. Travelled back to Rake's Bottom.

17. Discussed the garden with Merrydown, the gardener. I said I was loosing patience with weeds and took him into a quiet corner and asked him to look at my convolvulus — which was becoming uncontrollable and needed a strong man to keep it in order. Bending down he had a quick look and took out his rustic tool to prod it. Merry-down is a good gardener and very con-scientious, he said he would be quite able to tend it regularly, until I was satisfied. This I readily agreed to and look forward to having it done with some satisfaction.

20. Travelled down to Bournemouth. Staying at Boniface Tomnoddy's at Talbot Woods.

In the close covert of a grove,
By nature formed for scenes of love,
Said Susan in a lucky hour,
Observe yon sweet geranium flower;
How straight upon its stalk it stands,
And tempts our violating hands:
Whilst the soft bud as yet unspread,
Hangs down its pale declining head:
Yet, soon as it is ripe to blow,
The stem shall rise, the head shall glow.
Nature, said I, my lovely Sue,
To all her followers lends a clue;
Her simple laws themselves explain,
As links of one continued chain;
For her the mysteries of creation,
Are but the works of generation:
Yon blushing, strong triumphant flower,
Is in the crisis of its power:
But short, alas! its vigorous reign,
He sheds his seed, and drops again;
The bud that hangs in pale decay,
Feels, not, as yet, the plastic ray;
Tomorrow's sun shall bid him rise,
Then, too, he sheds his seed and dies:

But words, my love, are vain and weak,
For proof let bright example speak;
Then straight before the wondering maid,
The tree of life I gently laid;
Observe, sweet Sue, his drooping head,
How pale, how languid, and how dead;
Yet, let the sun of thy bright eyes,
Shine but a moment, it shall rise;
Let but the dew of thy soft hand
Refresh the stem, it straight shall stand:
Already, see, it swells, it grows,
Its head is redder than the rose,
Its shrivelled fruit, of dusky hue,
Now glows, a present fit for Sue:
The balm of life each artery fills,
And in o'erflowering drops distils.
Oh me! cried Susan, when is this?
What strange tumultuous throbs of bliss!
Sure, never mortal, till this hour,
Felt such emotion at a flower.

Richard Sheridan

"There is a tide in the affairs of women
Which, if taken at the flood, leads
God knows where."
Byron

Sand games

August

Aug. 24. Went bathing in the sea. We raised some eye-
brows amongst the rather prim people prom-
enading on the sands. I was using the same
bathing machine as Boniface and his friends,
Bryan and Michael. This was most definitely
frowned upon, as men and women are supposed
to use separate machines. What followed must
really have started things wagging and
probably caused a few maids to fall out of
their bath chairs, for while we were frolicking
in the water, playing games, Boniface's costume
came adrift. Neither of the others would play ball
so I had to help him back into his suit.
29. Back to Rake's Bottom.

"A little of what you fancy
does you good."
Marie Lloyd

September

September, the ninth month of the Gregorian calendar, but the seventh according to the old Roman calendar. The month changed its name a number of times, depending upon the whims of the Emperors who couldn't make up their minds. In the end Septimus, meaning seventh triumphed and so it was used to describe the modern ninth month.

Special Day. September 15. My birthday

"Gather ye rosebuds while ye may,
Old time is still a-flying:
And this same flower that smiles today
Tomorrow will be dying."

Robert Herrick

Mottoes for September.

"Man's love is of man's life a thing apart,
'Tis woman's whole existence."

Byron

Therefore love moderately: long love doth so
Too swift arrives as tardy as too slow.

Shakespeare

September

'Show me thy feet; show me thy legs, thy thighs;
Show me those fleshy principalities;
Show me that hill (where smiling love doth sit)
Having a living fountain under it.
Show me thy waist; then let me there withal,
By the ascension of thy lawn, see all.'

Herrick

September

Sept. 1. Glorious hot, sunny day. The countryside is a picture to be seen.

6. Geoffrey Nippleson took me racing at Titerton. He really is very handsome – reminds me of Horatio under his facial thatch. Had quite a flutter. I won on Free Love, while Geoffrey's filly came in second. On the way back to Rake's bottom we picniced by a lake. Had a lay in a large bed of reeds and watched a gorgeous sunset across the water.

10. John Thistlewort gave me a beautiful little black kitten.

12. Gathered heather from the common.

15. My birthday, which I declared a day of rest. I stayed in and played with my pussy.

21. Went to Wilberforce Renoir's exhibition in Bond Street. Made an appointment for him to paint my portrait. He suggested he did it in the nude. I thought it would make a change so I agreed.

25. Went to Wilber's studio. As I started to take off my clothes he came from behind a screen – starkers! I thought he was a bit forward, but I discovered that I had misunderstood him – he was to be nude as he worked better that way.

"I only know of two painters in the world; yourself and Velasquez. Why drag in Velasquez?"
Whistler

'She just wore
Enough for modesty – no more.'
R. W. Buchanan.

The General shows me his blade

October

The tenth month of the year was the eighth of the old Roman year~hence its name. It was sacred to the god Mars. The Anglo-Saxons knew it as Winter fylleth, because it was the start of fylleth~winter. It is the beginning of Autumn~when trees and bushes drop their raiments, revealing their nakedness.

Special Days.
> Oct 5. Day I first met H.H.
> Oct. 31. All Hallows Eve

Mottoes.

'In October sweet Autumn enters gently
With tresses of gold and brown.
And clothes that shield her modesty
Fall softly to the ground.'

"Then came October; full of merry glee."
Spencer

'In October dung your field
And your land will stink as well as yield.'

October

Oct.1. Warm, sunny day spent mainly in the garden.

2. Raining, dismal day. A letter from Horatio - he's on his way home at last. I wrote a long letter in reply. I do miss him so, inspite of all the attention I get from his friends.

7. Walked through Downwater Wood to Bishop's Pond; it's lovely at this time of year. Saw Ivy lying on the ground beneath a tree, couldn't see who was with her. I did not disturb them. Saw a heron rise, the pink and grey tints of his plumage contrasting against the brown of the trees. I wish I could paint like Hazel Sycamore. She painted a beautiful cock she saw standing bolt upright under some bushes. There is quite a variety of game in these woods.

13. Spending a few days with General Jeremiah Lancelot at his seat at Lower Sodbury. He is a great expert in ballistics, the science dealing with the motion of projectiles. He took me into a private room to see his special blade, which he kept carefully wrapped. Taking it from its packing, the General drew his weapon from its sheath. It must have been quite something in its day, but compared with others I have seen, and I've seen quite a few, it was a little dull and rusty, no doubt the worse for wear. The General had had it with him all his life. Seeing I was disappointed he let it slide back into the sheath again. We did not mention the tool of his trade again.

19. Rake's Bottom looks lovely in the brown and golden hues of autumn.

25. Went to a garden party at Phillip Limpney's estate at Penisbig Manor. We all assembled in the grounds to see his new erection, which has become notorious.

> 'This point pokes fun at all your pride
> Standing up proud and stout of heart
> Give in: be on the yielding side.
> This point pokes fun at all your pride.'
>
> P. Verlaine

October

Oct. 31. All Hallows Eve. October went out with a bang at Felicity Protocol's masqued ball at Belgrave Square. A most remarkable entertainment was provided in the form of a curious fig tree. It was in full foliage, but as the heat of the room reached the leaves, they curled up, dried quickly and fell to the ground, exposing the two trunks entwined together, the join scarcely perceptible. With an exclamation of surprise the tree split in two, revealing the Hon. Charles Leghorn and Penelope Laidwell ~ starkers. A round of applause relieved them of any further embarrassment and Felicity was complimented on such a novel entertainment. Although it started conventionally it soon turned into a full scale orgy, with everyone taking full advantage of their masks. I'm sure most of us would be at a loss to say who we spent our time with, unless of course we all disrobed again.

'If' all the young ladies who attended the ball were laid end to end, no one would be the least surprised.'

apologies to Dorothy Parker

" 'No, no; for my virginity,
When I lose that,' says Rose, 'I'll die;'
'Behind the elms, last night,' cried Dick,
'Rose, were you not extremely sick?' "

Matthew Prior 1664-1721

'One half of the world cannot understand the pleasures of the other.'

Jane Austin 1775-1817

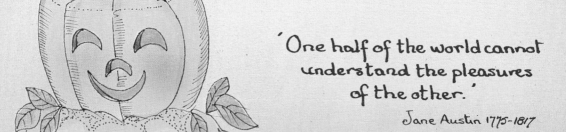

'Home is heaven and orgies are vile
But you need an orgy, once in a while.'

O. Nash

Hackneyed carriage and companion.

November

November, the eleventh month of the year, used to be the ninth month, under the old Roman decimal calendar system (they were very advanced). It was changed when their legendary King Numa, (700 B.C.) reshuffled the months and invented the Roman 'dozen' calendar of twelve months, adding two more, January and February ~ just to confuse the populace. The Anglo-Saxons thought it a bloody month and went out and slaughtered their cattle so they wouldn't starve in the winter.

Special Days.
       Nov. 5. Guy Fawkes' Gunpowder Plot
       Nov. 9. His Majesty's Birthday
       Nov 22. St Cecelia
       Nov 29. Thanksgiving Day in America.

Mottoes.

"Remember, remember prick not in November,
Sharp thorns do the roses still bear.
Take care where you slumber, take heed where you lie.
For to tangle with thorns in the chill of November
May tell a round, tubby tale in July."

"If there's ice in November that will bear a duck
There's nothing else to do but stay in and sleep."

November

1. A dull, wet November day. Winter is here.

5. Spent the afternoon walking in the woods. In the evening celebrated Guy Fawkes at Jeremy Ilsington's cottage on the edge of Rake's Bottom. A number of people were there - huddled together around the bonfire, and we all joined in letting off fireworks. The men had rockets and Roman candles and each woman had two sparklers.

9. His Majesty's birthday. The King is a charming man. I remember him from a brief encounter when I attended the Duke of Drummond's balls. He and Horatio have met on a number of occasions - he is most interested in exploring.

15. A cold, bright day. Violet looked radiant. Went for a walk in the wood. Now that most of the flowers have bloomed and wilted the fungi are noticable, pushing up their pink phallic like stalks through the brown mantle.

20. Went to London to stay at Dorothy Huckworthy's.

22. St Cecelia's. David Deadwood, an <u>old</u> friend of Horatio's, took me to the opera. On the way back to his chambers he made a rather pathetic grope in the dark of the carriage as he looked for his wallet. The opera was La Traviata which was boring, but not so boring as his Triviata which he tried later. It was a real let-down, such a long, drawn-out performance, but then it never had a firm base in the beginning. He knows nothing about music and is no composer.

29. Went to the American Embassy for a Thanksgiving Ball. I was the guest of Daniel Rockergirl III. He was charming and invited me back to his house to see his oil-well bonds.

30. Back at Rake's Bottom. I went for a walk in Brackelsham Wood to pick some nipplewort. The ground was thick with fallen leaves and the holly already has its bright red berries.

November

"Pretty lute, when I am gone
Tell thy mistress here was one
That hither came with full intent
To play upon her instrument."
                              Traditional

"And she prescribed, so kept we crotchet-time,
And every stroke in order like a chime,
Whilst she, that had preserved me by her pity
Unto our music framed a groaning ditty."
                              Thomas Nashe

"I've oft been told by learned friars,
    That wishing and the crime are one,
And Heaven punishes desires
    As much as if the deed were done.

If wishing damns us, you and I
    Are damned to all our heart's content;
Come, then, at least we may enjoy
    Some pleasure for our punishment!"
                              Thomas Moore 1779-1852

"A man is as old as he's feeling,
A woman as old as she looks."

                Mortimer Collins 1827-1876

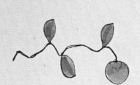

DECEMBER

The last month of the year. Its name is derived from the fact that it was the tenth month of the old Roman system. It was the winter month of the Saxons, the Yule monath. At Christmas or Yule tide there is an ancient custom of kissing under the mistletoe ~ I find that nowadays men don't wait for this but find plenty of other opportunities.

Special Days.
   Dec. 25. Christmas Day
   Dec. 31. New Year's Eve

Motto.

  'Bounce upon the velvets dear
  Christmas comes but once a year,
  When it comes kiss and fuddle dear
  For when its gone, its old beer.'

December

Dec. 1. A bright, cold and clear day. The frost has brought numerous tits and a robin to the suet and nuts near the kitchen window.

4. Changeable day, quite cold. A letter from Horatio he will be home in January.

8. I'm getting quite excited about seeing Horatio again in the New Year. Although his friends have all rallied round and tried to make up for his being away, they can in no way replace him. Still, they have been so nice and most accomodating, that after a year I'm really quite exhausted.

15. Went to the Kinema at Worthington-under-mann with Spencer Leaky. In spite of it being quite cold, he kept me very warm — but it was a bit of a struggle.

18. Heavy snow storms over the last few days have clad the countryside in a mantle of white, making everything look most festive.

20. I went to Canon Sozleword's at the Rectory to help put up the decorations. Old Weedmonger, the Church-warden, nearly made a bloomer. While I was up the ladder he slipped and nearly defrocked me. The dear old Canon was quite content to pass me his balls, which one must admit were most decorative, but were somewhat fragile. I had to handle them very carefully — but they did look nice dangling on the tree.

27. Travelled to Inebreate Hall at Chippingsodbury, to celebrate the New Year. I was greeted at the station by Arum, still as wild as ever, and delighted to see Violet again. Everyone was there, including Geoffrey Pinchbottom (no longer the shy boy he was). Lord Clutterbuck was as charming as ever.

30. Rested all day, saving myself for New Year's Eve.

"Love ceases to be a pleasure,
when it ceases to be a secret."
Aphra Behn

Canon's balls

December

"There is only one thing in the world worse than being talked about, that is not being talked about."
Wilde

I take my diary and I look,
And see this year an open
book.
A book that only I shall read
And chuckle at in times of need.
When I am old and past my prime,
I'll look with longing at this
time.
E.H.

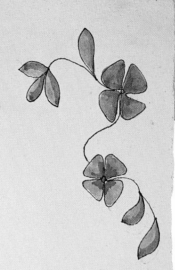

Here's to the roses and flowers that bloom,
To me in your arms and you in my room;
A door that is locked and a key that is lost,
And a night that's a thousand years long.